STOP SMOKING IN 5 MINUTES

Dr Chris Williams

First published in 2008 by Five Areas.
This edition first published in 2012 by Darton, Longman and Todd Ltd
1 Spencer Court, 140–142 Wandsworth High Street, London SW18 4JJ.

ISBN 978-0-232-52919-7

A catalogue record for this book is available from the British Library.
Printed and bound in Great Britain by Halstan & Co Ltd, Amersham.

Although we hope you find this book helpful, it's not intended to be a direct
substitute for consultative advice with a healthcare professional, nor does
the author or the publisher give any assurances about its effectiveness in a
particular case. Accordingly, neither the author nor the publisher shall be held
liable for any loss or damages arising from its use.

DARTON·LONGMAN +TODD

IT'S GOING TO BE EASY

Er, isn't it supposed to be hard?

Hard compared to what?

Learning to ride a bike? Stopping smoking is easier than that. Mastering French? Easier than that. Sticking to that exercise regime so you look good on the beach? Everything is easier than that!

And not only is it going to be easy, it's also going to be enjoyable. Instead of having a smoke 20 (or more) times a day, you're going to do something you like, 20 times a day.

And after about 4 weeks, you'll be well on the way to beating cigarettes.

ARE YOU SERIOUS ABOUT THE 5 MINUTES?

Absolutely.
You can stop smoking
if you do it 5 minutes
at a time.

If you've tried stopping before, you'll know how it feels to be desperate for a cigarette. It's a real craving and you can't think of anything but lighting up.

That craving lasts about five minutes on average, and this is true whether it's caused by nicotine addiction, habit, or one of those problems or events that always trigger the thought: "I need a cigarette".

To stop smoking, all you have to do is get through those 5-minute spells, one by one, until they go away.

It might take a few weeks. Even a bit longer. But it doesn't matter, because when you can beat those cravings, you've beaten cigarettes.

OK, WHAT DO I DO TO BEAT THEM?

You do Your Thing

A craving is a thought or feeling that pops into your head and tries to make you want a cigarette.

It tries hard, too. It gives you the shakes, messes with your mouth and can even make you feel sad, nervous or irritated, just to trick you into lighting up – that's its thing.

But now you've decided to stop smoking, it's no longer **Your Thing**.

So here's what you do:

Next time you feel a craving coming on, follow this simple plan and you'll get through its nasty short life without doing what it wants.

SAY HELLO

SAY GOODBYE

DO YOUR THING

We call it the Simple Stopping System, but we're like that. Turn over and say hello to the first part of the SSS.

SAY
HELLO
CRAVING

"You'll be gone in 5 minutes!"

When you notice a craving coming on, mentally step back, see it for what it is, and let it know you've rumbled it.

"Hello craving. You're trying to make me smoke, but you can't. And you'll be dead in 5 minutes!"

When you treat a craving this way, it loses most of its power over you.

By knowing it's there, naming it and remembering that it won't last long, you've taken control of the situation.

SAY GOODBYE

"Not today, thank you!"

Now speak to the craving again,
saying "I'm not doing your thing,
I'm doing *My* Thing, so goodbye",
and turn your back on it.

Don't challenge it or try to argue
with it, don't think about it any
more, just let it be. A craving loves
attention, so don't give it any.

And move on to do **Your Thing.**

DO
YOUR
THING

Do my what?

Your Thing is something you do that's enjoyable and takes 5 minutes. It could be anything – it's your choice (we'll show you examples of other people's Things later on).

You might prepare a 5-minute meditation. Maybe you could look through family photos to remember why you've stopped. You might recite a favourite poem to yourself, or memorise a new one. You could read part of a book, play music, do press-ups with a friend, learn to draw, write a letter, touch your toes, do a crossword or sudoku.

There are just two rules –
Your Thing must last about 5 minutes (like a craving), and it must be enjoyable or useful (unlike a craving).

You want to draw a chalk circle on the carpet and dance naked? Who are we to argue? It's **Your Thing.**

There are some more ideas on the next page.

Learn how to Juggle

Meditate for 5 minutes

Jogging Up Stairs

Other People's Things

Drink a glass of water

Compose a Haiku

Barbershop Duet Practice

Go round the World

Learn a New Word

HAIKU?

Do push-ups for 5 minutes

Learn to Play the banjo

Joke book

Learn a New Joke

Rinse a Vest!

15

NOW LET'S CHOOSE YOUR THING

It can be almost anything

…so long as it takes just 5 minutes and you enjoy it. This is **Your Thing** and you need to really get into it, every time you do it.

So what do you love to do?
What have you always promised yourself?
What could be the focus of your mind?
What could you achieve in a whole lot of 5 minute chunks every day?

Imagine! You could learn Italian or master origami or practice the piano or knit a woolly hat or get really good at shuffling cards with one hand… and stop smoking at the same time!

Have a cuppa, give it some thought, and write **Your Thing** here.

My Thing is:

....

....

....

NOW CHECK YOUR THING

Things come in all shapes and colours and it's different strokes for different folks, of course. But you do need to make sure of a few points to have the best chance of stopping smoking in 5 minutes.

Score 5 ticks on the list opposite and you're all set to do **Your Thing.**

My Thing will last 5 minutes

Cravings last less than 5 minutes, so **Your Thing** should be the same. If it's a long-term idea, like learning a language or making something, you must be able to break it up into 5-minute chunks.

I will enjoy My Thing

Don't try to do something you hate 20 or more times a day – that's the old way to stop smoking. Make sure **Your Thing** is at least pleasant and, if you like, also useful.

I'll look forward to My Thing

You're going to be doing **Your Thing** a lot at first, so think how you might feel on the third day – will you be raring to read another two pages of that thriller? Or will you be thinking "Oh no, not naked dancing again".

I have what I need to do My Thing

Got that poetry book? Sketch pad? Written your list of reasons or made that pocket-sized photo album of the children?

I know when I'm going to do My Thing

You need a definite start date. Pick one now and have a very good excuse if it's not tomorrow. You're going to do enjoyable things for an extra hour each day – why wait?

WHAT ABOUT PATCHES, PILLS AND GUM?

Go for it!

They all can work, so if you want to give yourself an even better chance of success, combine our Simple Stopping System with something else.

You can buy nicotine patches, gum or lozenges over the counter at the chemists or you can get pills like Champix (Varenicline) and Zyban (Buproprion) on prescription.

Some people swear by hypnotism or acupuncture and you can find out about all these options from your doctor, or your chemist. You could also try some online research.

Doing **Your Thing** is a great way to stop smoking.

Combining it with other stuff makes it even greater.

BUT WHAT IF I SLIP?

Get up again

Remember, you're stopping 5 minutes at a time, so if you do have a cigarette, you'll only have slipped for 5 minutes.

Don't beat yourself up - remind yourself of the Simple Stopping System and get ready to beat that next craving by doing a little something you enjoy, 10 or 20 times a day.

And if it doesn't feel very enjoyable, maybe **Your Thing** needs to be more fun. Go back a few pages and choose a new one.

Or go to
www.llttf.com
for more examples.

THE SIMPLE STOPPING SYSTEM

SAY HELLO

When you notice a craving coming on,
mentally step back, see it for what it is,
and let it know you've rumbled it.

Say "Hello craving. You're trying to make me
smoke, but you can't. And you'll be dead in
5 minutes!"

SAY GOODBYE

Say, "I'm not doing your thing,
I'm doing **MY** thing, so goodbye!" and turn
your back on the craving.

Don't challenge it or try to argue with it, don't
think about it any more.

DO YOUR THING

Read that book, write that poem, say those
lines, learn that verse, draw that picture, knit
that hat, check that list of reasons,
look at those pictures, shuffle
those cards, fold that paper,
dance that dance.

GOOD LUCK!

WHERE TO GET EVEN MORE HELP

This little book is one of a series by Dr Chris Williams that helps you deal with the challenges that life throws at you. There are books for depression, anger management, low self-esteem, low energy and enthusiasm, cutting down drink and more. There's one that can help you fix almost everything, like getting a job, making friends or getting out of debt, and there's even one that can help you get rid of bad thoughts.

All the books are backed up by a website

www.llttf.com

where you can use free audio and video courses and also connect with other people who have similar problems.

http://www.canstopsmoking.com
http://www.ashscotland.org.uk
http://www.quit.org.uk
http://smokefree.nhs.uk

Free book: How to stop smoking and stay stopped
http://www.healthscotland.com/documents/312.aspx

ABOUT THIS BOOK

With websites receiving over 4 million hits a month and a wealth of supporting research data, the Five Areas Approach on which this book is based, devised by Dr Chris Williams, is one of the most widely-used CBT systems in the world.

Cognitive Behavioural Therapy (CBT) has a strong evidence base for helping people with low mood, anxiety and a growing range of other common mental and physical health difficulties.

Want to learn more about you? Turn things around in your life for the better? The Five Areas Approach can help you to do this. It takes the proven CBT model and makes it accessible and practical so that you can have the tools you need to help change things in your life – fast.

Please visit the Five Areas websites – www.llttf.com (free life skills course), www.llttfshop.com (bookshop) and www.fiveareasonline.com (online books) – to discover more about this work and see the other resources on offer.

Dr Chris Williams is Professor of Psychosocial Psychiatry at the University of Glasgow, UK, and is a past-President of the British Association for Behavioural and Cognitive Psychotherapies (www.babcp.com) – the lead body for CBT in the UK, trustee of the charities Anxiety UK and Triumph over Phobia and is a well-known CBT workshop leader and researcher.

PICK ME UP

Turn your life around – fast!

DARTON·LONGMAN+TODD

Please visit www.dltbooks.com for more information.